For Larson,
with all my love.

ISBN: 978-1-913339-38-8
Text copyright – Michaela Dias-Hayes 2022
Illustrations copyright – Michaela Dias-Hayes 2022

COLOUR and ME!

By Michaela Dias-Hayes

First published in the UK
January 2022 by Owlet Press
www.owletpress.com

Painting with my fingers is my favourite thing to do.

I wonder what will happen, if I mix yellow, red and blue?

If I mix red with yellow . . .

I love to pick oranges . . .

straight from the tree,

If I mix yellow with blue . . .

. . . I get green.

Yes, it's true!

You can say 'hello', Myrtle . . .

. . . she's my nosy, green turtle.

If I mix blue and red together . . .

. . . I get purple.

Let's paint
for ever!

Purple grapes taste very sweet.

The perfect 'share-with-Nanny' treat!

If I mix red and yellow and blue . . .

Brown is MY colour.

This is ME.

This colour suits me . . .

PERFECTLY!

I made orange, green and purple,
using yellow, red and blue —
and brown from all three colours!

"What a
magical thing
to do!"

Nanny says that every colour . . .

. . . is special, just like me.

And now I know, I really hope . . .

. . . that all of you agree!

The Colour Wheel